£7.99

G000299548

Welcome To Looney Tunes Annual 2012

™

This annual belongs to:

Age:

Favourite Looney Tunes character:

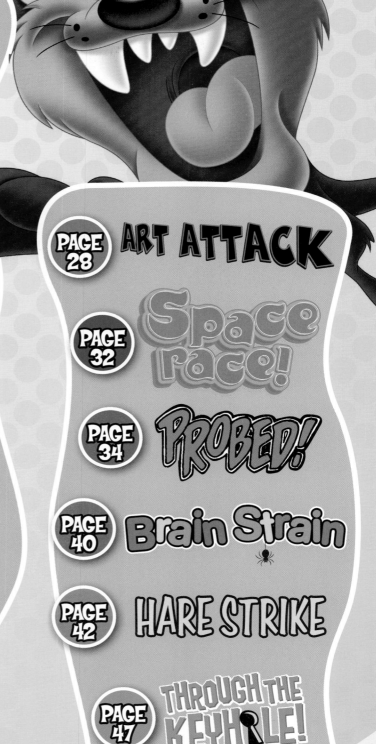

Make a Splash

Can you spot the 8 differences between these two underwater scenes?

STEP TO IT

Which set of footprints belong to each Looney Tune?

WRITE YOUR ANSWERS IN THE BOXES!
1 2 3 4 5

BROWN HAWK DOWN

EARL KRESS
WRITER
DAVID ALVAREZ
PENCILLER
MIKE DECARLO
INKER
PAT BROSSEAU
LETTERER
DAVE TANGUAY
COLORIST
HARVEY RICHARDS
ASST EDITOR
JOAN HILTY
EDITOR

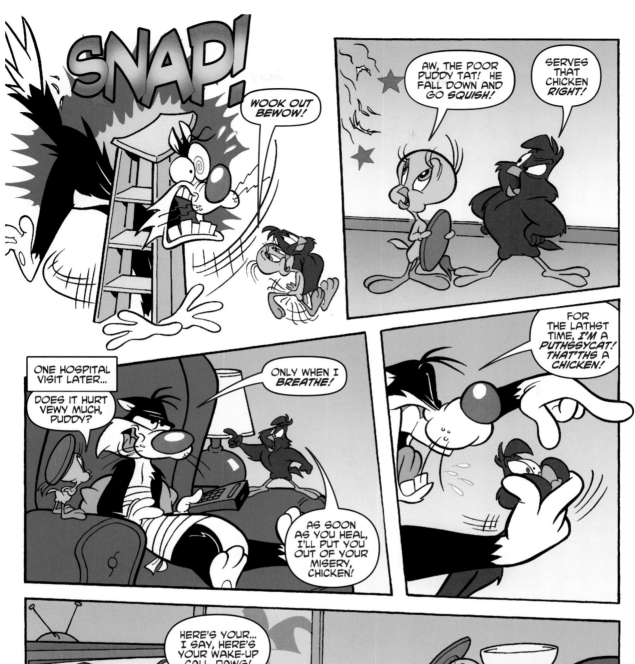

It's Behind You!

Can you match Pepe Le Pew up with his shadow?

A   B   C   D   e   F

Write your answer here!

➡

Dotty Daffy!

Join the dots to work out
what Daffy is up to!

Add some colour
to Daffy once you've
joined the dots.

15

ELMER'S HOME IMPAIRMENT

HEWWO, FAITHFUL VIEWERS, AND WEWCOME TO MY SHOW! *TODAY'S* PWOJECT IS SOMETHING THAT YOU CAN MAKE TO PWOTECT OUR WITTLE FEATHERED FWIENDS DURING THE COLD, HARD WINTERS--

A *DEWUXE* BIRDHOUSE!

BYE-BYE BIRDHOUSE

DAVID CODY WEISS- WRITER
DAVID ALVAREZ- PENCILS
MIKE DeCARLO- INKS
RYAN CLINE- LETTERER
DAVE TANGUAY- COLORIST
DIGITAL CHAMELEON- SEPARATIONS
HARVEY RICHARDS- ASST. EDITOR
JOAN HILTY- EDITOR

AND AS ALWAYS, *"HOME IMPAIRMENT"* IS BWOUGHT TO YOU BY THE GOOD FOLKS AT *ACME.*

WEMEMBER ACME-- WHEN YOU WEAWWY NEED TOOLS IN THE *WORST* WAY!

ACME

HEWE'S A FINISHED VERSION. DOESN'T THAT WOOK *COMFY?*

DOESN'T IT JUST *BOWL YOU OVER?*

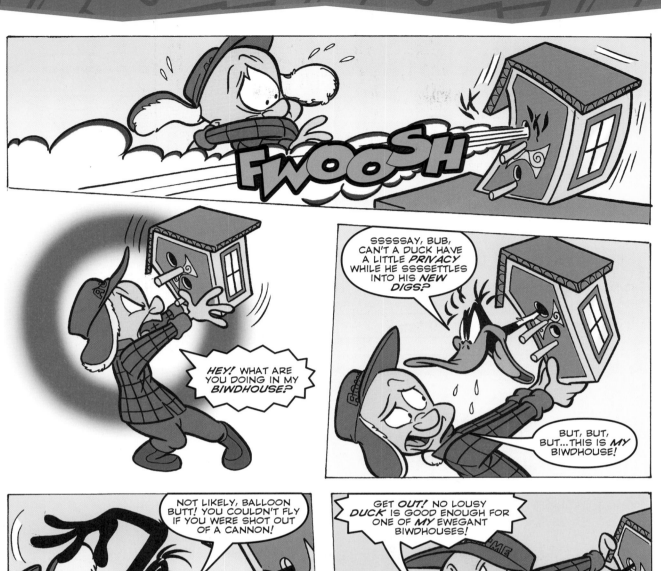

CONTINUED ON PAGE 22

Duck and Dive

Brighten up your boring old desk with this awesome Daffy Duck desk tidy!

YOU WILL NEED:

One medium-sized cardboard box, four small cardboard boxes, thick card, newspaper, sticky tape, PVA glue, paints and a paintbrush

1 Cut off the top flaps from the largest cardboard box. Now cut the two shorter sides of the box at an angle.

2 Take the four smaller boxes. These will make the storage sections inside the desk tidy. Cut the top and one side off each of the four smaller boxes.

3 Tape three of the boxes inside the big box. Tape one box to the front. Cover the whole thing with two layers of papier maché and leave it to dry.

4 Draw Daffy's head shape onto card and cut it out. Glue it to the back of the box.

5 Paint the desk tidy with your favourite colours. Paint Daffy with black, white and orange paint.

6 Once it is dry, you can finish decorating your desk tidy. Add Daffy's name, some stars and Daffy silhouettes using black paint and a thin paintbrush. Now your Daffy desk tidy is ready to use!

DRAW TAZ

Follow these steps to draw your own Taz-tastic picture. Use a pencil to draw the steps so you can erase any mistakes.

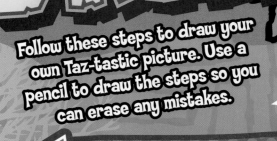

1

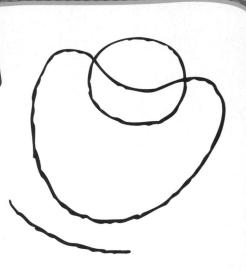

Start with a circle. Add a heart shape over the circle and a curved line underneath.

2

Add lines to show the position of his arms. Sketch in two curved lines underneath his body for the position of his tornado legs! Join his body to the tornado section.

3

Add two circles for his hands. Sketch a big "W" for his mouth.

4

Add some detail to his mouth and nose. Sketch in two shapes for his paws.

5

Add the details to his fingers. Sketch in his ears and eyes.

6

Draw in his teeth and tongue and the swirly lines on his tornado legs.

7

Once you are happy with your sketch, draw over it in black pen and rub out the pencil lines.

Now draw your own spinning Taz to complete the scene below!

WB# 1876

KA-BLAMMM

ART ATTACK

LIEBMANN --WRITER
ALVAREZ --PENCILLER
DECARLO --INKER
GARCIA --LETTERER

TANGUAY --COLORIST
DIGITAL --SEPS
RICHARDS --ASST. EDITOR
HILTY --EDITOR

SURE-FIRE BIRD CATCHING PLAN #328,756; EXPLODING CHICKEN.

ACME THINKING CAP

Boosts your I.Q. 1000%

SKIZZZIK

WHOOMM

WHOMP

Cut out the two counters below.
Throw a dice and whoever scores highest
will move first. Start at the planet Mars and take it
in turns to move around the game board.
The first player to arrive at Earth is the winner.

©WBE (s09)

©WBE (s08)

14

You take
a wrong turn at
The Milky Way.
Go back to
space 12.

15

16

17

18

13

19

Stop to chat
to an alien.
Miss a turn

20

12

11

Hitch a ride
with a shooting
star. Take
another turn.

21

finish

33

Writer: Dave King Penciller: Nelson Luty (Sol Studio) Inker: Horacio Ottolini Letterer: John Costanza Colorist: Prismacolor

35

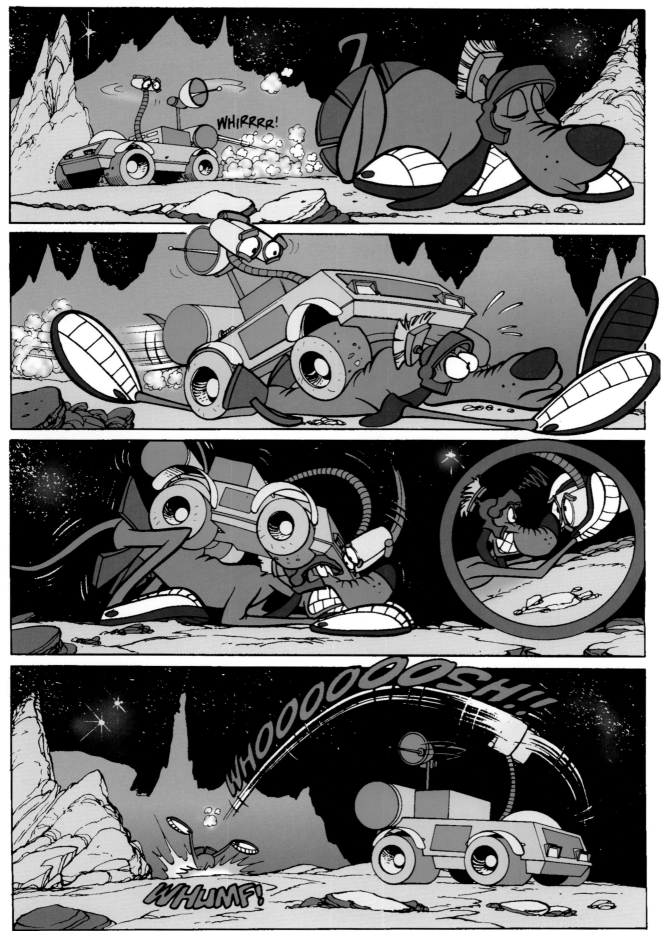

Brain Strain

Test your brain cells with this fun game!
Study the scene for one minute and then cover the page.
Now have a go at answering the tricky questions on the opposite page.
Good luck!

40

Now you have studied the scene, try your luck at answering these questions. Good luck, doc!

BOO!

BOO!

1 Which Looney Tune is dressed in a blue wizard costume?

2 What is sitting on the doorstep?
A) a black cat
B) a pumpkin
C) an owl

3 What number is next to the front door?
A) 1 B) 44 C) 1313

4 True or false Bugs Bunny is in the picture.

5 How many pumpkins are on the steps?

6 What sort of hat is Taz wearing?
A) a top hat
B) a beret
C) a bobble hat

7 What colour is Gossamer, the big hairy monster in the doorway?

8 True or false Taz is eating a sandwich

Answers: 1) Sylvester. 2) B. 3) C. 4) False. 5) 2 pumpkins. 6) A. 7) Red. 8) False.

HARE STRIKE

SHOLLY FISCH- WRITER
WALTER CARZON- PENCILLER
HORACIO OTTOLINI- INKER
RYAN CLINE- LETTERER
DAVE TANGUAY- COLORIST
DIGITAL CHAMELEON- SEPARATIONS
HARVEY RICHARDS- ASST. EDITOR
JOAN HILTY- EDITOR

LOONEY TUNES 81. October, 2001. Published monthly by DC Comics, 1700 Broadway, New York, NY 10019. POSTMASTER: Send address changes to LOONEY TUNES, DC Comics Subscriptions, P.O. Box 0528, Baldwin, NY 11510. Annual subscription rate $23.88. Canadian subscribers must add $12.00 for postage and GST. GST # is R125921072. All foreign countries must add $12.00 for postage. U.S. funds only. Copyright © 2001 Warner Bros. All Rights Reserved. LOONEY TUNES characters, names, and all related slogans and indicia are trademarks of Warner Bros. The stories, characters and incidents mentioned in this magazine are entirely fictional. Printed on recyclable paper. Printed in Canada.
DC Comics. A division of Warner Bros.—An AOL Time Warner Company

CONTINUED ON PAGE 48

THROUGH THE KEYHOLE!

Can you work out who Bugs Bunny can spy through each of these keyholes?

① ② ③

④ ⑤ ⑥

A) Sylvester
B) Tweety
C) Wile E. Coyote
D) Foghorn Leghorn
E) Pepe Le Pew
F) Granny

47

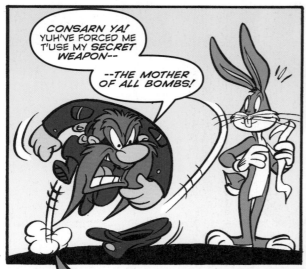

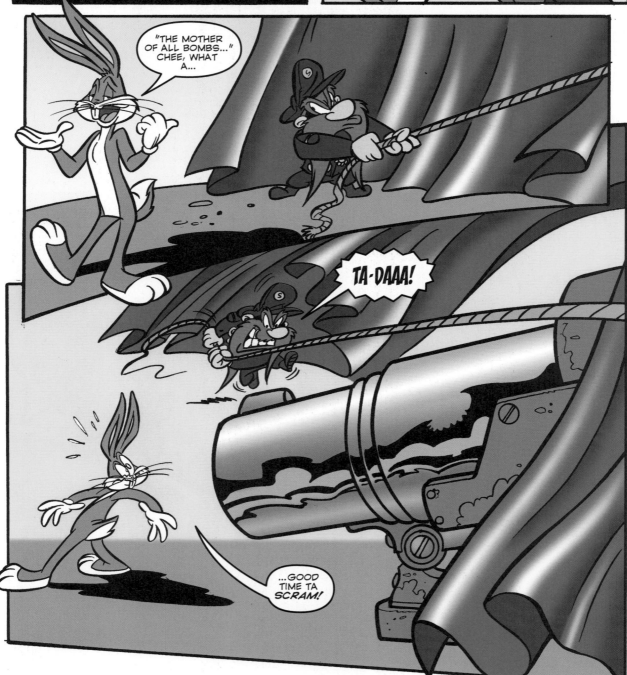

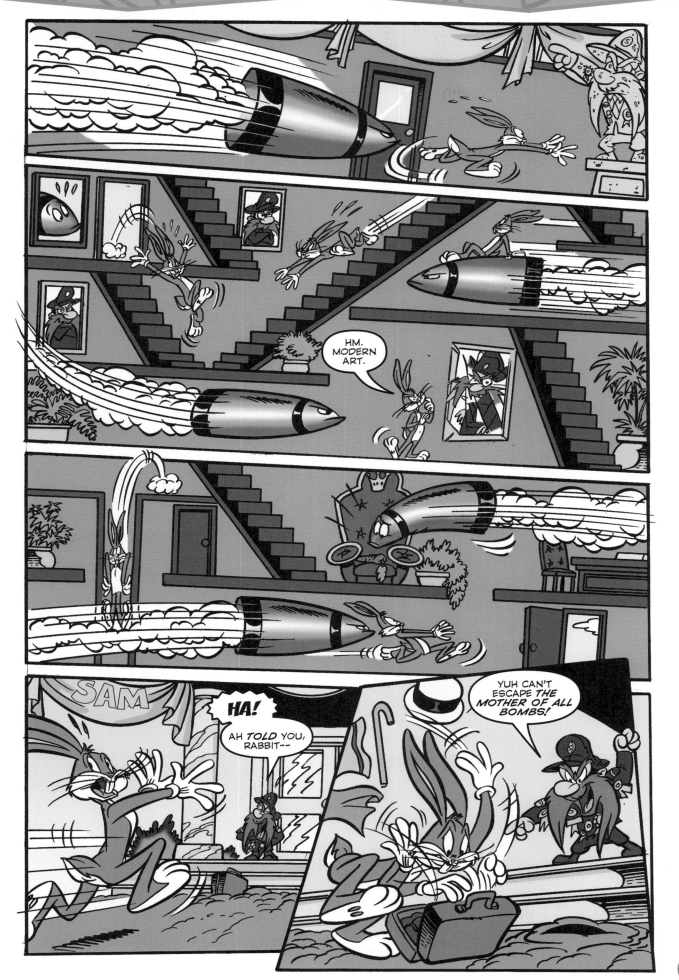

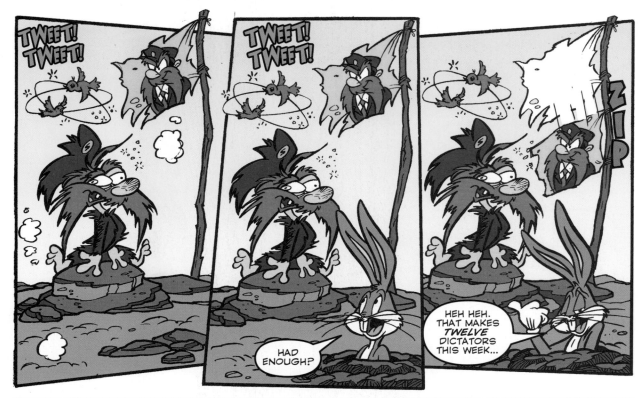

ANIMAL MAGIC

Granny is at the pet shop, can you spot all of the pets hidden in the grid?

OPEN

Goldfish
Parrot
Kitten
Hamster
Mouse
Guinea Pig
Chinchilla
Snake
Gerbil Dog
Rabbit

G	U	I	N	E	A	P	I	G	S		
R	O	H	A	M	S	T	E	R	N		
A	U	L	I	B	R	E	G	E	Y		
B	R	S	D	E	C	K	T	I	D		
B	L	E	A	F	S	T	E	P	O		
I	O	O	N	A	I	U	D	E	G		
T	S	N	A	K	E	S	O	L	E		
T	O	R	R	A	P	F	H	M	E		
C	H	I	N	C	H	I	L	L	A		

53

LOONEY TUNES 117. October, 2004. Published monthly by DC Comics, 1700 Broadway, New York, NY 10019. POSTMASTER: Send address changes to LOONEY TUNES, DC Comics Subscriptions, P.O. Box 0528, Baldwin, NY 11510. Annual subscription rate (12 issues) $27.00. Canadian subscribers must add $12.00 for postage and GST. GST # is R125921072. All foreign countries must add $12.00 for postage. U.S. funds only. Copyright © 2004 Warner Bros. Entertainment Inc. All Rights Reserved. © 2004 Warner Bros. Entertainment Inc. LOONEY TUNES and all related characters and elements are trademarks of and © Warner Bros. Entertainment Inc. (s03) The stories, characters and incidents mentioned in this magazine are entirely fictional. Printed on recyclable paper. DC Comics does not read or accept unsolicited submissions of ideas, stories or artwork. Printed in Canada.

DC Comics, a Warner Bros. Entertainment Company